Printed and Published in Great Britain by D. C. Thomson & Co., Ltd., 185 Fleet Street, London EC4A 2HS.

(Certain stories do not appear exactly as originally published.)

ISBN 0-85116-528-1

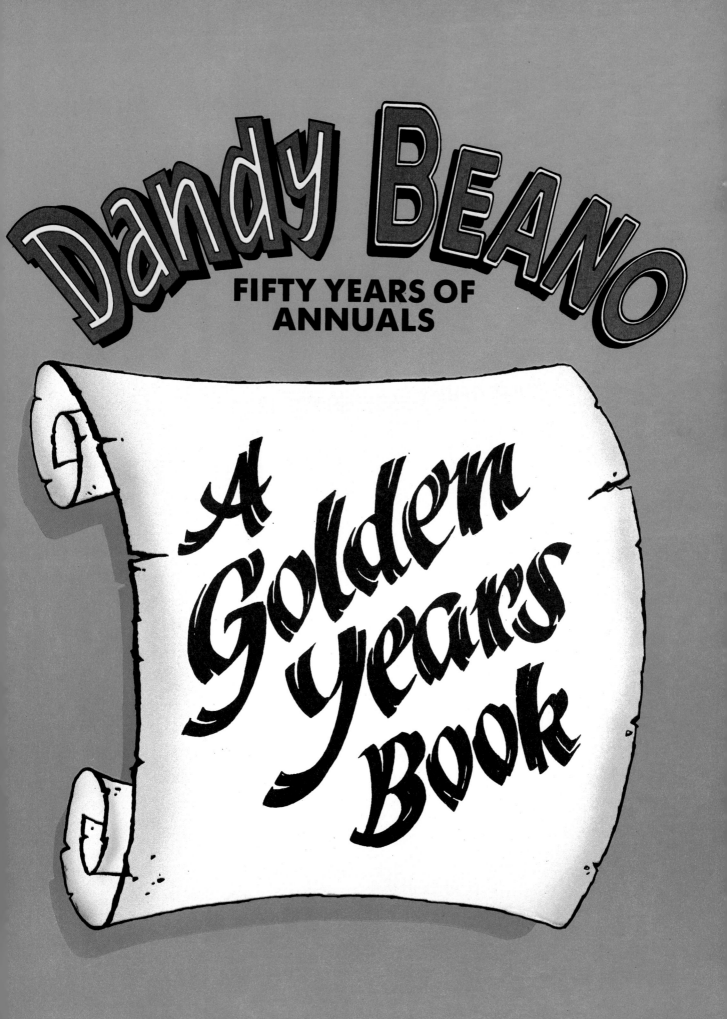

Dandy BEANO

FIFTY YEARS OF ANNUALS

A Golden Years Book

1971
The year astronauts took a drive across the moon, Desperate Dan took a drive across town that drove the sheriff crazy.

1949
Animal antics galore with big Eggo the Ostrich, Biffo the Bear, and Koko the Pup. Only an ass would miss it.

1951
Which comic character was even smaller than Tom Thumb? Step forward, or fly forward . . . Freddy the Fearless Fly.

1967
Laughs ahoy, when Winker Watson and his pals from Greytowers School set sail on a cruise. Be prepared for gales of laughter and a storm in a tea-cup.

Your guide to the best and brightest moments selected from over 100 Dandy and Beano annuals.

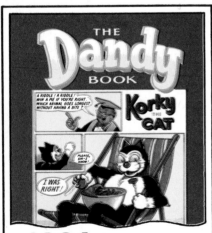

1964
Even the Dandy doesn't feature talking fish, but in '64, Korky The Cat met the next best thing when he went in search of a fishy snack.

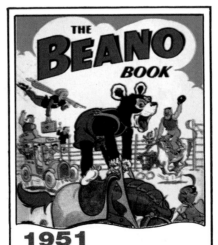

1951
The bear facts! Three pages of Biffo the Bear, Beano's bruin superstar, and the wildest fun in The West with Ding Dong Belle.

1958
A right royal treat with Davy Crockett, King of the Wild Frontier and Prince Whoopee, the boy who was so powerful he could play the world's biggest game of noughts and crosses.

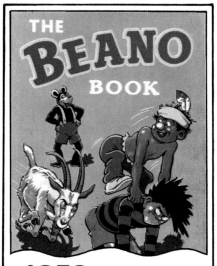

1959
Minnie The Minx drives a Mini, Little Plum lands a plum job, but Lord Snooty's anything but snooty, thanks to his down-to-earth chums.

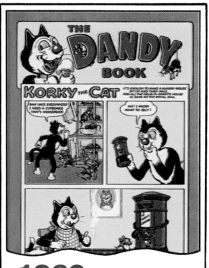

1960
This book's a smasher in every sense. Enjoy three pages of The Smasher plus five featuring Tin Lizzie, the robot maid, made of metal.

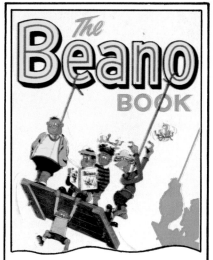

1963
When The Bash Street Kids took a trip to Scotland and met The Loch Ness Monster, guess who got the bigger fright.

STORY

1958
The face that beams out at you on just about everything from t-shirts to towels was a big star with his own annual, 'way back in the '50s.

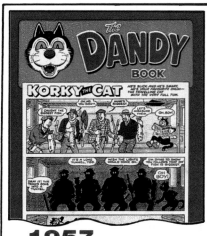

1957
A chance to meet two of the comic world's earliest superstars — Hungry Horace and Keyhole Kate. By 1957 they had already been entertaining young readers for 20 years.

1972
If you think your school's rough, you ain't seen nuthin' yet. Read about a teacher who wore a suit of armour, and discovered his pupils didn't like 'knight' classes.

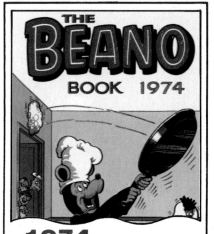

1974
Enjoy a guided tour of Beanotown — home of the comic's stars. And if that isn't enough, how about a music lesson from The Bash Street Kids.

AN ANNUAL EVENT

When teenage American boxer, Cassius Clay, won a gold medal at the 1960 Olympic Games in Rome, one of the most remarkable careers in sporting history was launched.

Within the next four years, young Cassius defeated Sonny Liston to become World Heavyweight Champion and changed his name to Muhammad Ali. And that was how the world would know him for the rest of his highly successful and often controversial career.

And when it came to packing a punch in the 1960 comic scene, stories didn't come any punchier than the 'Smasher' below.

THE SMASHER

NOW TURN OVER AND SEE WHAT HAPPENS

What's the largest number of times Korky's face has appeared in a single Dandy story? Don't know? Well, start counting because this particular cat's tale is almost certainly the record-holder.

1960

The Dandy superstars of 1960 were a crazy crowd. The guy below is Screwy and the girl on the opposite page is nuts . . . well nuts, bolts and metal plates to be accurate. Meet Tin Lizzie, the metal maid, and her equally hard-headed pal, Brassribs the butler.

Tin Lizzie now had a giant catapult — and the weapon she chose to fire was one of the skis thrown away by Brassribs.

Carefully she took aim. This must be a direct hit.

It was! The hurtling ski hit Brassribs such a wallop that the skating butler was rocketed into the air.

Cartwheeling over and over, Brassribs plummeted down. CRUNCH! Clean through the ice.

Brassribs felt far from cool as he pulled himself out of the freezing water. "Lizzie!" he snarled, his eyes agleam with vengeance.

Picking up the ski that had done the damage, Brassribs charged with it at Lizzie.

Lizzie picked up the other ski and charged at Brassribs. Holding the skis like lances, the two antagonists pounded full tilt towards each other.

CRASH! "Take that, you brass-necked ruffian," roared the maid. "Down with you, you rusty old dish-washer!" rasped Brassribs, breaking his ski against Lizzie's head. Soon both skis were smashed.

Still the battle raged on. Tooth and nail they fought — and they did fearful damage to each other.

Five minutes later it was all over. The battlers had battered each other to pieces. Young Bertie came along. "Gosh!" he gasped. "They look as if they've been run over by a train."

Bertie picked up the bits and piled them on his sledge. It would be some job repairing this lot.

Professor Puffin set to work at once. He couldn't do without servants.

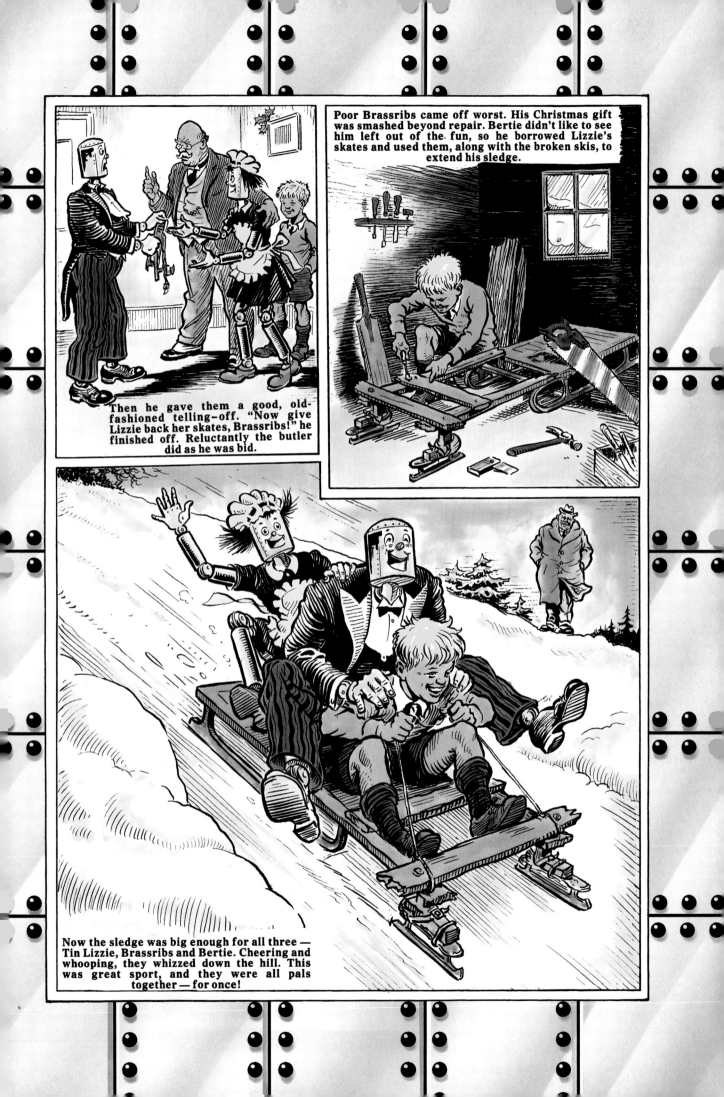

Then he gave them a good, old-fashioned telling-off. "Now give Lizzie back her skates, Brassribs!" he finished off. Reluctantly the butler did as he was bid.

Poor Brassribs came off worst. His Christmas gift was smashed beyond repair. Bertie didn't like to see him left out of the fun, so he borrowed Lizzie's skates and used them, along with the broken skis, to extend his sledge.

Now the sledge was big enough for all three — Tin Lizzie, Brassribs and Bertie. Cheering and whooping, they whizzed down the hill. This was great sport, and they were all pals together — for once!

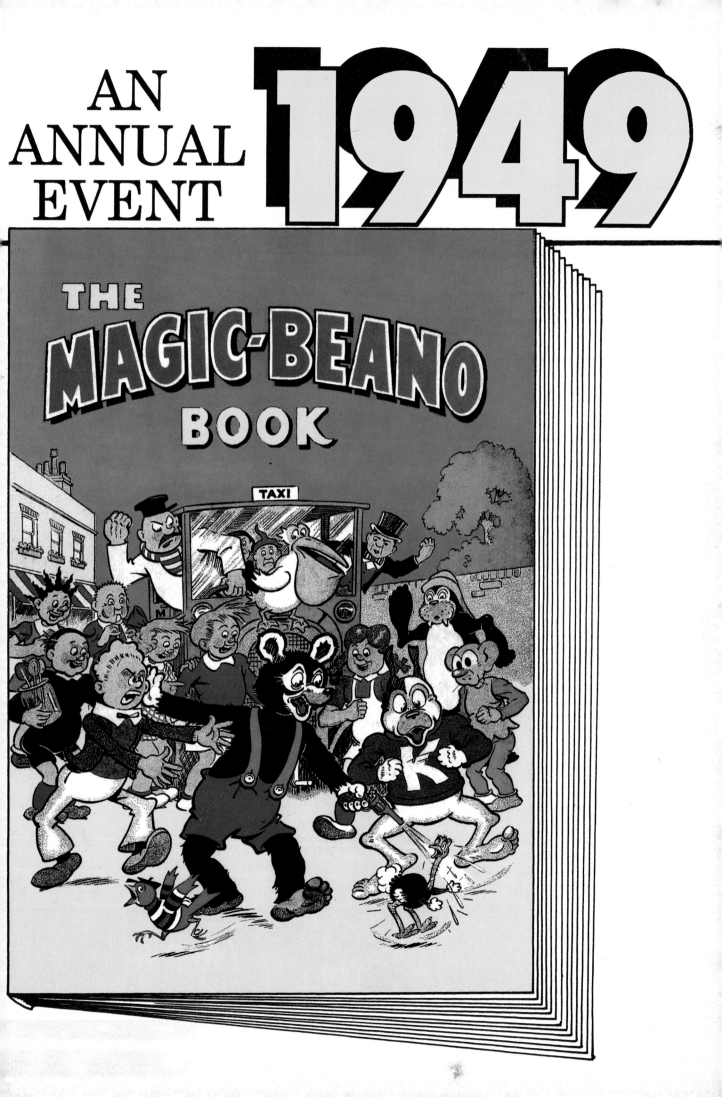

AN ANNUAL EVENT
1949

Which Hollywood star had the wettest nose? No, not Gene Kelly while he was 'Singing In The Rain'. The answer's Lassie. This sheepdog superstar enjoyed a string of hit movies during the 1940s, and '49 was a vintage year for canine epics. Two films appeared, "Challenge To Lassie" and "The Sun Comes Up". The latter co-starred another Hollywood legend, Jeanette MacDonald.

But it wasn't only on the silver screen that animals found fame. The Beano Book of 1949 was packed with doggy tales, bear facts and ostrich antics featuring Koko the Pup, Biffo The Bear and Big Eggo.

AN ANNUAL EVENT

1949

This hilarious illustration was the title page (first page) of the 1949 Beano Book. The 'Magic' in the name refers to the short-lived Magic comic, which was the original home of Koko The Pup.

AN ANNUAL EVENT

When the United States Army called up Elvis Presley, the rockin' and rollin' had to take second place to rallying round the flag. And soon even The King's most devoted fans were forced to admit that their wild hero had been well and truly tamed.

Maybe Dennis the Menace's long-suffering father should have enlisted the might of the military to help control his son. In 1958, Dennis not only ran riot in The Beano Book, but he also had all 80 pages of his very own annual for mischief, mayhem and menacing.

COMIC CLASSICS

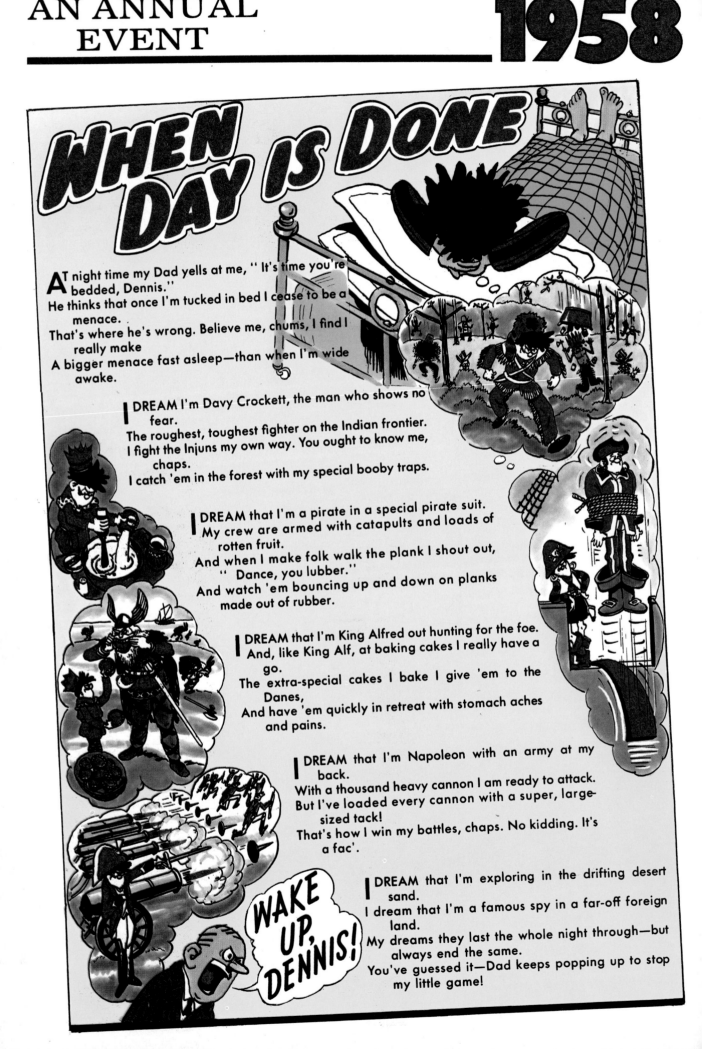

WHEN DAY IS DONE

AT night time my Dad yells at me, " It's time you're bedded, Dennis."
He thinks that once I'm tucked in bed I cease to be a menace.
That's where he's wrong. Believe me, chums, I find I really make
A bigger menace fast asleep—than when I'm wide awake.

I DREAM I'm Davy Crockett, the man who shows no fear.
The roughest, toughest fighter on the Indian frontier.
I fight the Injuns my own way. You ought to know me, chaps.
I catch 'em in the forest with my special booby traps.

I DREAM that I'm a pirate in a special pirate suit.
My crew are armed with catapults and loads of rotten fruit.
And when I make folk walk the plank I shout out, " Dance, you lubber."
And watch 'em bouncing up and down on planks made out of rubber.

I DREAM that I'm King Alfred out hunting for the foe.
And, like King Alf, at baking cakes I really have a go.
The extra-special cakes I bake I give 'em to the Danes,
And have 'em quickly in retreat with stomach aches and pains.

I DREAM that I'm Napoleon with an army at my back.
With a thousand heavy cannon I am ready to attack.
But I've loaded every cannon with a super, large-sized tack!
That's how I win my battles, chaps. No kidding. It's a fac'.

I DREAM that I'm exploring in the drifting desert sand.
I dream that I'm a famous spy in a far-off foreign land.
My dreams they last the whole night through—but always end the same.
You've guessed it—Dad keeps popping up to stop my little game!

WAKE UP, DENNIS!

Who's almost as big a menace as Dennis? Only Beano's Minnie The Minx comes close. And in this story, Minnie came too close for comfort as far as Dennis was concerned.

1958

COMIC CLASSICS

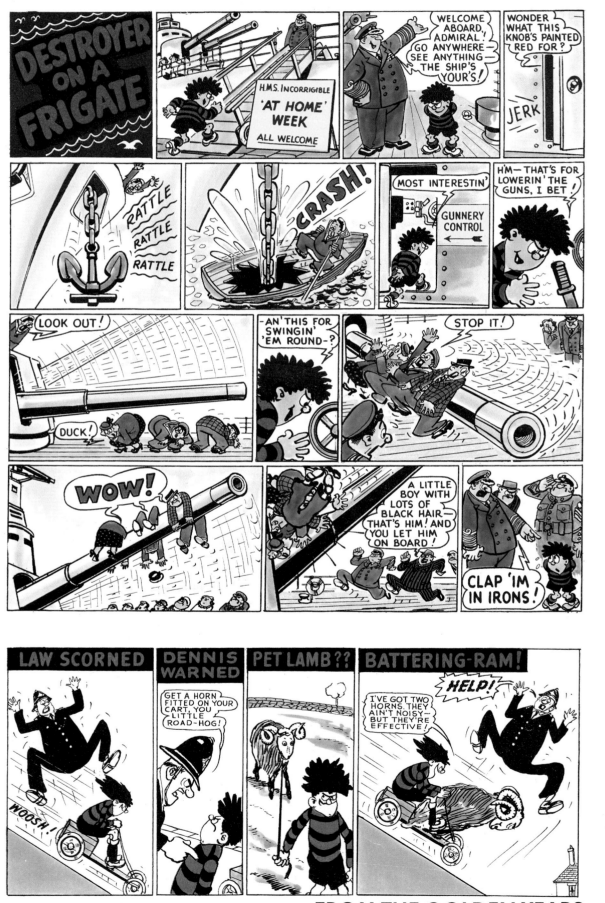

1958

During the 1950s Davy Crockett became a hero to a brand new generation of young movie fans thanks to Fess Parker's portrayal of the legendary American frontiersman. But Davy Crockett's adventures weren't restricted to the big screen. Readers of the 1958 Beano Book were treated to this exciting tale.

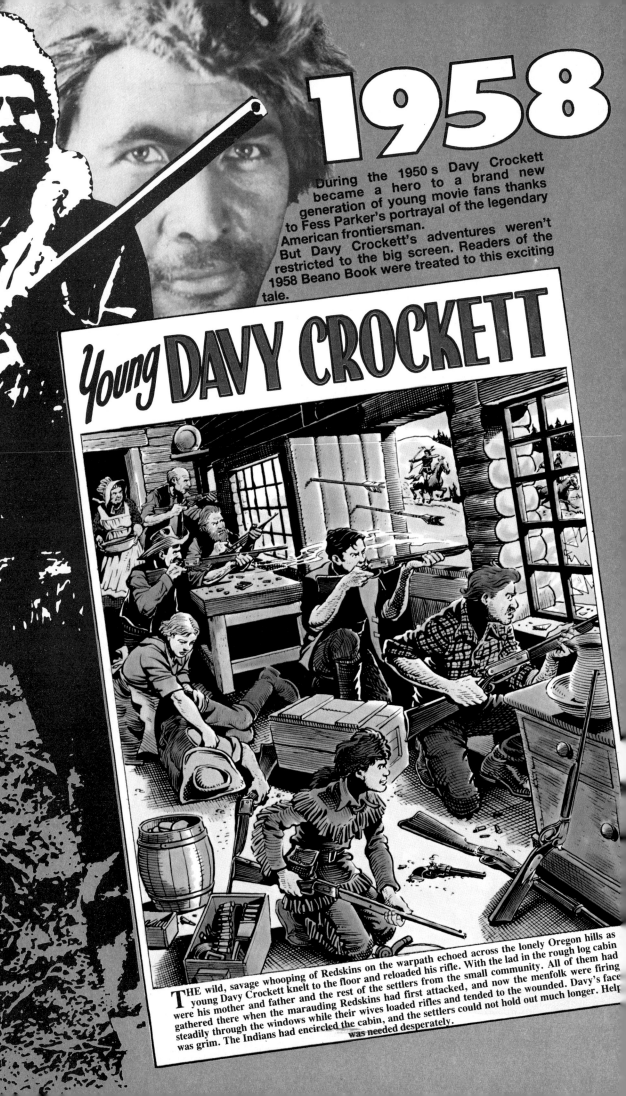

Young DAVY CROCKETT

THE wild, savage whooping of Redskins on the warpath echoed across the lonely Oregon hills as young Davy Crockett knelt to the floor and reloaded his rifle. With the lad in the rough log cabin were his mother and father and the rest of the settlers from the small community. All of them had gathered there when the marauding Redskins had first attacked, and now the menfolk were firing steadily through the windows while their wives loaded rifles and tended to the wounded. Davy's face was grim. The Indians had encircled the cabin, and the settlers could not hold out much longer. Help was needed desperately.

AN ANNUAL EVENT

1958

2 — Davy came to a quick decision. He would bring help to the besieged settlement. Before his father could stop him, the lad picked up his trusty catapult, to which was attached a fishing reel, and ran out through the back door of the cabin into the open.

3 — Next second, Davy had overturned the rain barrel standing against the wall of the cabin and crawled inside. Slowly, then with ever-increasing speed, the barrel began to roll towards the swift-flowing river at the foot of the rocky slope.

4 — The Redskins were not fools and were quick to realise that someone was inside the rolling barrel. Several arrows zipped through the air after Davy, but all flew wide and the barrel rolled on unchecked.

5 — Then, at last, the speeding barrel reached the edge of the river bank. Splash! The barrel landed in the water and began to drift quickly downstream. But young Davy was not out of danger yet — far from it!

6 — Some of the mounted Redskins followed the drifting barrel along the river bank, and three of their arrows thudded into the wood, perilously close to Davy's head. But the lad was unharmed and, slowly, the barrel was carried into the middle of the stream.

7 — When he was well out of range of the Redskins' arrows Davy peered over the edge of the barrel. He knew what to expect. The swirling barrel was being carried towards foaming rapids where it would be smashed to matchwood by the jagged rocks!

8 — Davy had not a moment to lose if he was to escape with his life. Swiftly he loaded his catapult with the weighted end of a fishing line attached by its reel to the catapult handle. Then he took quick aim and fired. The line snaked into the air.

9 — Davy's aim had been true, and the line fell over a stout branch jutting out from a tree on the river bank. Holding the catapult firmly, the lad grasped the end of the line in his other hand and pulled himself out of the barrel. Just in time!

10 — Using the rocks as stepping stones, Davy swung himself to the river bank. Suddenly a Redskin galloped into view, his tomahawk at the ready. Davy raced away and threw himself behind a large rock.

11 — Precious time was being wasted. Davy had to shake off the Redskin. Then, on the opposite side of the trail, he saw a rattlesnake sunning itself on a rock. Davy's heart leapt. He had thought of a plan.

12 — But Davy had to work fast and, quickly, the lad again fitted the weighted end of the line to the sling of his catapult. The Redskin was only a scant few feet from the rock when Davy fired at the deadly snake and caught it with the fish-hook.

13 — The Redskin loomed over Davy, his tomahawk ready to strike, as the lad tugged on his fishing line. A split-second later, the wriggling snake was pulled from its place on the rock to drop in front of the Indian brave's horse. That did it!

14 — With a shrill whinny of terror, the horse reared up into the air, unseating its rider. Leaving his catapult lying on the ground, Davy jumped to his feet and grabbed the frightened horse's bridle. Next second he was astride the horse and urging it forward.

15 — Giving the horse its head, Davy galloped off along the trail. The outwitted Redskin's tomahawk sliced through the air after the lad, but fell far shot of its mark. Like a streak of lightning, the lad thundered away. Nothing could stop Davy now!

16 — Half an hour's hard riding and Davy had reached Fort Dawson, a United States cavalry headquarters. Breathlessly the lad gasped out his news. A few minutes later a troop of cavalry was ready to leave.

17 — At a gallop, Davy led the soldiers out of the fort to the small, besieged settlement in the hills. His sabre drawn, the officer in command led his men in a fierce cavalry charge. The Redskins were routed.

18 — As the last surviving members of the Redskin war party galloped out of sight, the settlers came out from their log-cabin stockade. Detailing some of his men to follow the escaping braves, the officer prepared to lead the remainder of his cavalry troop back to Fort Dawson. "Good-bye, Davy!" he said, saluting. "We owe a lot to you. You're a brave lad!" The boy glowed with pride and returned the salute. Thanks to a catapult, young Davy Crockett had saved the hard-won settlement from destruction.

At the time of the comics' golden anniversaries, anyone who had the cheek to suggest that Dandy and Beano were fifty years old was told in no uncertain terms that they were in fact... FIFTY YEARS YOUNG!

And just to prove it, Dandy and Beano have gone on to produce weekly comics and annuals that are as fun-packed as any in their long and glorious history.

1964

In 1964 it was pirates who ruled the waves . . . the airwaves. Radio Caroline, Britain's first pirate radio station, started broadcasting non-stop pop music from a ship moored in the North Sea, out of the authorities' reach. Soon Caroline had several competitors, all offering their own brand of off-shore pop radio.

But when it came to ruling the Dandy, there was no doubt that Korky was the top dog, oops, top cat, as you can see in these scenes opposite.

1964

Dandy has always liked to start an annual and finish it with a big laugh. And they don't come much bigger than the scenes here and overleaf that opened and closed the '57 Dandy book.

1974

Two of the movie scene's biggest names, Paul Newman and Robert Redford, shared the honours in 1974 when "The Sting" won "Best Picture" award at the Oscar ceremony in Hollywood.

And if Hollywood's where you find movie stars, where do comic stars live? Beanotown of course! And we've even provided a map.

LITTLE PLUM

CHIEFY

NIBBLE!

MINNIE

THE NIBBLERS

MUNCH!

GRAND-FATHER CLOCK HOUSE

DANNY

PLUG

GRANDPA

DODGES VOL II

DODGES

DODGES

'ERBERT

FATTY

SPOTTY

ROGER

MILK

BASH ST. KIDS

SMIFFY

TINKLE! TINKLE!

CRIMP!

YEEEAGH!

I DON'T THINK MUCH OF YOUR SINGING, TEACHER!

CUTHBERT CRINGEWORTHY ISN'T PLEASED—

PAH! I CAN'T COMPOSE ON THIS OLD WRECK. I'LL ASK MY UNCLE'S FIRM TO SEND ROUND A BETTER PIANO.

SMACK!

SOON—

PIANO FOR MASTER CRINGEWORTHY.

TO CUTHBERT LOVE FROM UNCLE

BOOMF!

1967

In 1967, Britain was flying high. Sandie Shaw won The Eurovision Song Contest, in Vienna, with 'Puppet On A String'. Also that year, Concorde, the supersonic jet airliner, was unveiled, giving the press and public their first glimpse of the remarkable plane.

And when it came to the best of British, Dandy's Winker Watson was undoubtedly one of the country's top dodgers, tricksters and wanglers. The proof's in this story from the '67 Dandy Book.

The DANDY BOOK 1967

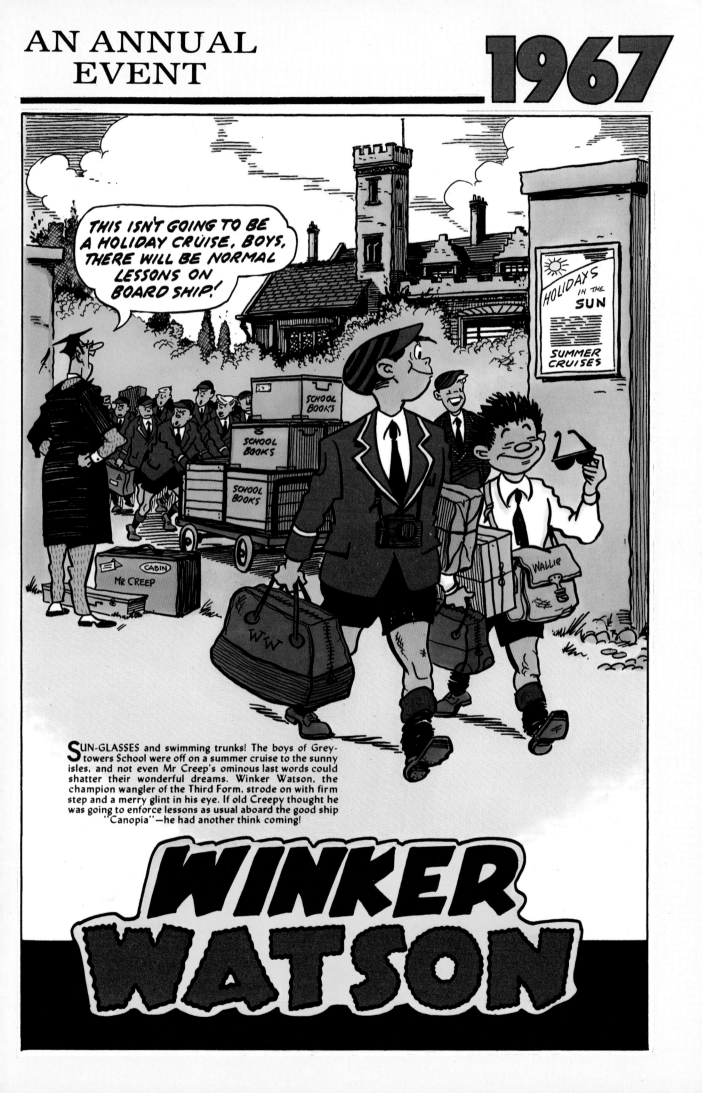

Winker had a few little things to do before he went aboard, such as making certain that all school books would go right to the bottom of the hold, and that certain other boxes would go to the classroom!

Creepy started putting Africa on the blackboard from memory.

And while his back was turned, the class put most of those pork pies completely off the map!

Eyes in the back of his head! That's what Creepy should have had when in charge of a hungry class like this.

The Head had been dishing out extra lessons. Now he was about to be taught a lesson himself. First his cigars were purloined, with the aid of a gluey block on a fishing line.

Then the bold Winker replaced them with a different box.

There were "sharks" in the pool, and a boy pirate behind Creepy with a cutlass, tickling the master with the sharp end. It seemed to the ship's officers that here at last was a schoolmaster with real spirit, one who could have fun with his pupils. He was putting on such a fine act of being scared, too, wasn't he?

And the Third Form master really was scared. He was scared of heights, and sharks, and water, and cold steel, and he was wishing he had never chased that black-masked pirate who had pinched his loud-hailer. And here came the Head, bellowing in his loud voice, just as the boy pirate tickled Creepy with the point again!

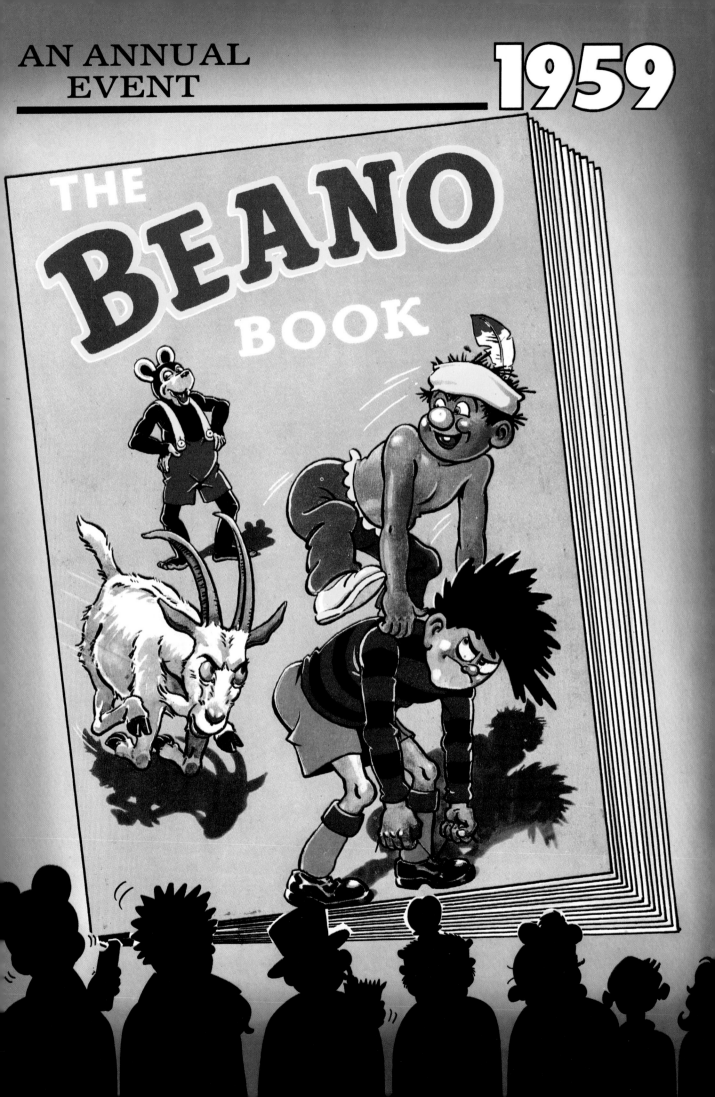

The Mini, the little car with the big reputation, first appeared on Britain's roads in 1959. Costing £500 and capable of 70 miles per hour, the small car was such a big hit that while other models constantly altered their appearance over the years the Mini remained virtually unchanged.

Another "Mini" popular in '59 was Beano's tiny superstar . . . Minnie The Minx. She also changed remarkably little and readers of today's Beano will have no problem recognising their heroine .

1959

As the popularity of the Dandy and Beano grew, comic fans clamoured for even more chances to read about their fun-pals. This led to the publication of "spin-offs" — annuals devoted to one particular character or story. For the record, you'll find the details overleaf.

In 1949, the year records were shrinking to the now familiar seven inch size, Dandy was expanding its range of publications with the introduction of a Black Bob Book. This proved to be the first of eight solo outings for the Dandy Wonder Dog.

1955 was the year British television introduced adverts which raised money to finance programmes. 1955 also saw the appearance of an annual full to the brim with the escapades of a wild young lad whose adventures were financed by his DAD'S money — in the shape of bills for breakages! Dennis the Menace, of course! Since 1955 Dennis books have appeared at regular intervals, without a break — but with plenty of breakages!

1953

In 1953, the first James Bond spy novel was published. Cool, suave Commander Bond was a real tough guy — but none came tougher than the Dandy's cow-pie-chomping Desperate Dan! In the same year Dan's very own annual was a big seller with readers who preferred pie stories to spy stories.

1979

FROM "THE BEANO"

THE BASH STREET KIDS

1930

In 1979, Margaret Thatcher created a record when she became Britain's first female Prime Minister, and took charge of the country. Unfortunately, Teacher, of "Bash St Kids" in the Beano, was rarely in charge, as could be seen in their very first annual on sale that year. Bash Street Kids Books are now an annual event!

AN ANNUAL EVENT **1972**

Mark Spitz, a 22-year-old Californian swimmer, made sporting history when he won an incredible seven gold medals at the 1972 Munich Olympics. In the pages of that year's Dandy Book only Desperate Dan could match Mark's muscles of steel, but one other comic star did wear a metal suit. And you can find out why a village teacher needed armour in the story opposite.

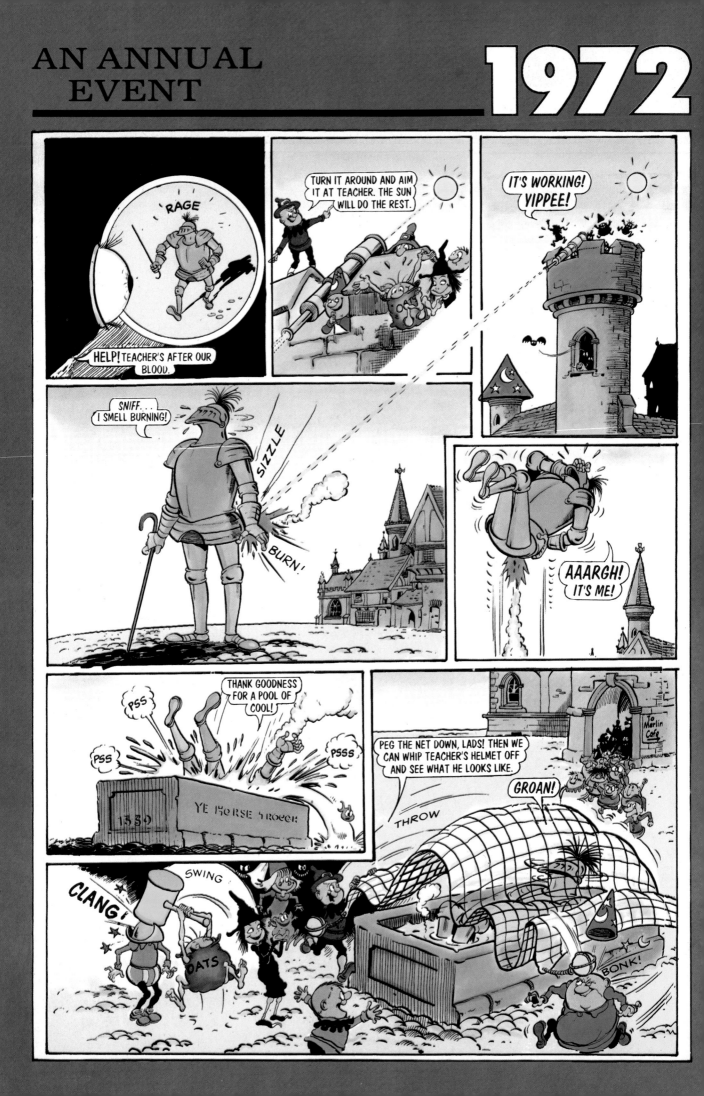

AN ANNUAL EVENT

Thousands flocked to London's South Bank in 1951 to visit The Festival of Britain. After years of shortages and rationing, visitors to this huge exhibition were delighted to discover pavilions packed with exciting and colourful designs for everything from fabrics and furniture to plastic tableware. There were a few long faces that year however, and surprisingly they belonged to the Beano bunch. It seemed to have something to do with Biffo's singing. But it wasn't long before Britain's best-loved bear quietened down, and that cheered up his fellow funsters. Soon Biffo was wearing a big bright smile and a kilt to match.

1951

THE **BEANO** BOOK

PETER PIPER
~ AND HIS MAGIC PIPES ~

WHEN Peter plays his pipes, you know, all statues come to life — Presto! Today he's off to have a lark or two down in the local park. Young Pete had better have a care. The keeper doesn't want him there. But Pete has seen Sir Francis Drake carved out of stone. Now that's a break. Pete plays his pipes. Well, bless my soul! Now Drake's alive complete with bowl! The bowl goes flying straight and true. Well bowled! The keeper's feeling blue.

2 — The keeper's chasing poor old Pete. Pete puffs and pants, for he's dead beat. He plays his pipes. Gosh! He's no dunce. That scarecrow comes to life at once. Immediately he starts to scrap. He turns and socks the keeper chap. Then off he runs with Pete. Hooray! It seems that they will get away. Alas, our Pete's to get no peace. Here's what he dreaded — the police!

3 — Now Peter and his scarecrow chum are both downcast and feeling glum. For they are trapped by all their foes. Perhaps they'll go to jail. Who knows? How will the pair escape? Here's how. They're near an inn — the Flying cow. Pete plays his pipes. He's doing fine. Now see what's happened to that sign. The Flying Cow's alive today, and it's all set to fly away. Pete's on its back. He's won at last. Thanks to the pipes, the danger's past.

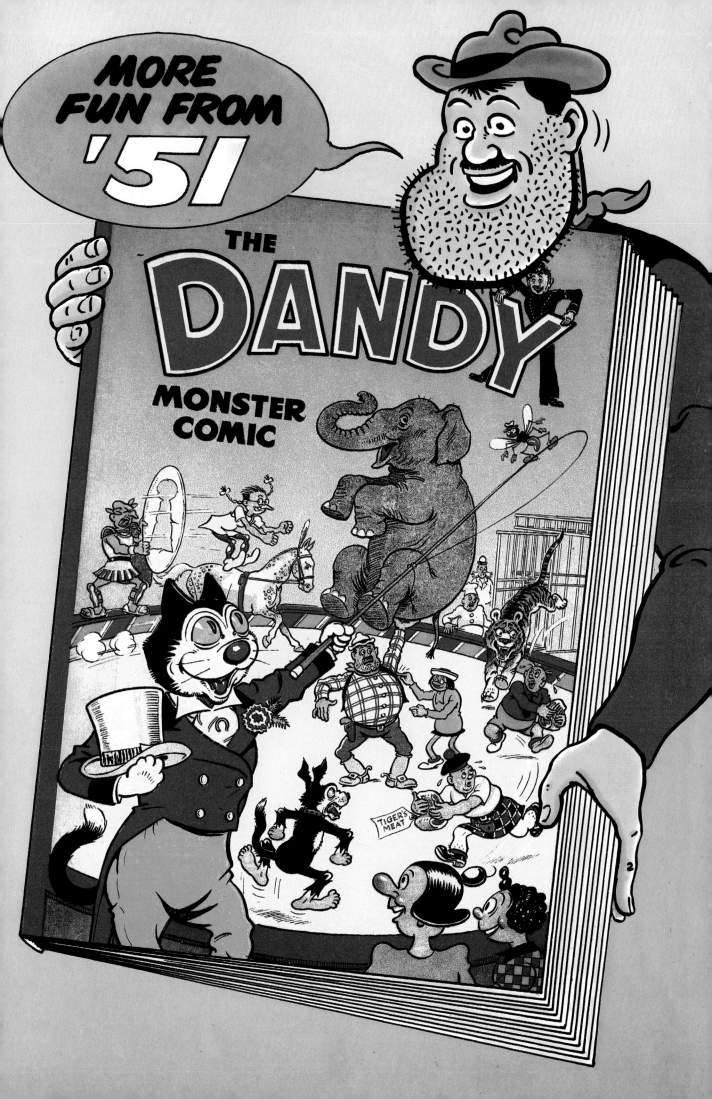

Freddy's not the only thing that flies — so does time! We've almost reached the end of the book, but we're going out in style. The last section features some of Beano's best-loved stars from a vintage period for British comics, the early 1960s.

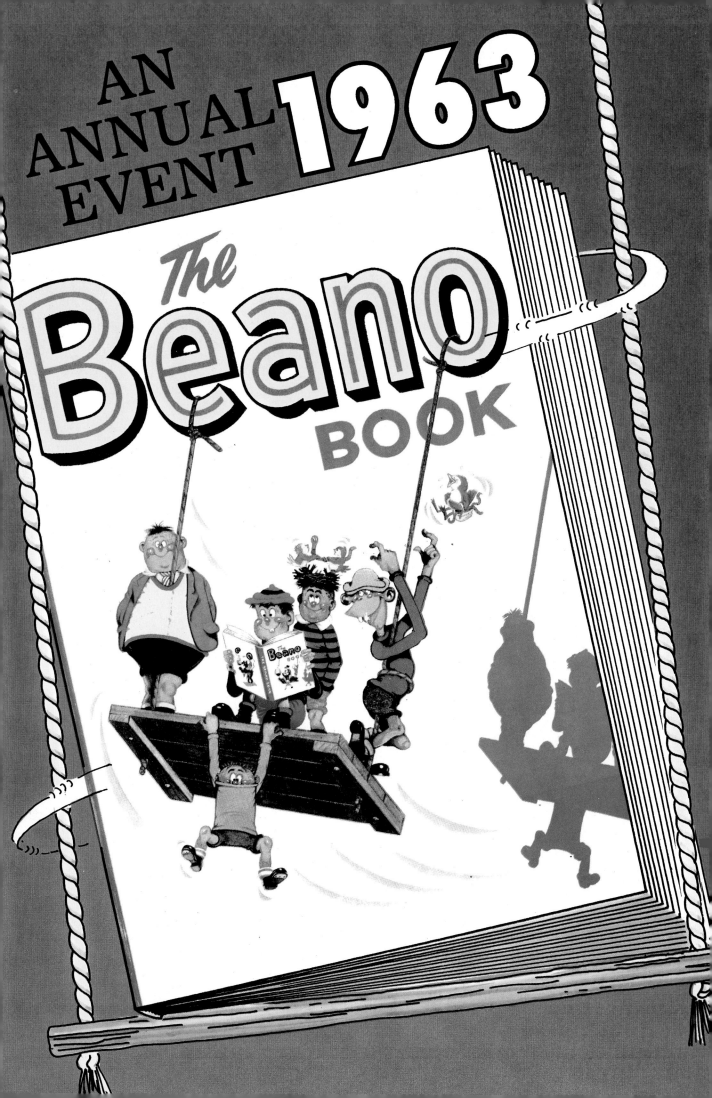

Does Dandy dumbfound you or Beano bamboozle you? They may do, if you're looking at one of their early annuals and wondering how old it is. That's because none of the books carried dates until the mid 1960's. Now you can use this annual spotter's guide to identify and date any Beano or Dandy book, and if you're lucky enough to have some, look after them, as they're now collectors' items.

DANDY BOOKS

YEAR   DESCRIPTION OF COVER

1939 — Korky pointing to other Dandy characters.

1940 — Korky hanging upside-down on a trapeze.

1941 — Korky leads a musical procession.

1942 — Desperate Dan swimming, towing other characters in a boat.

1943 — Korky leading others on bicycles, Desperate Dan on steamroller.

1944 — Korky on ball kicked by Desperate Dan.

1945 — Korky on skis, Desperate Dan on pair of tree-trunks.

1946 — Dandy characters in star-shapes.

1947 — Korky tossed in blanket by other characters.

1948 — Korky using other characters as puppets.

1949 — Korky with cigar, top hat. Desperate Dan carries his luggage.

1950 — Korky pours kettle of hot water into sea.

1951 — Korky as circus ringmaster.

1952 — Korky's toy shop, with clockwork Dandy characters.

1953 — Korky tricks mice with parcels.

1954 — Korky hides fish under top hat.

1955 — Korky fishing using his tail.

1956 — Korky's joke shop sign-painting.

1957 — Korky on train luggage rack, stealing fish.

1958 — Korky catches fish with magnet.

1959 — Korky sails in canoe, then umbrella.

1960 — Korky uses pillar-box as pantry.

1961 — Korky balances egg on nose.

1962 — Korky under lamp-post, frying bacon and eggs.

1963 — Korky looks through port-holes.

1964 — Korky in deckchair, eating pie.

1965 — Korky pours itching powder on a pantomime horse.

BEANO BOOKS

YEAR   DESCRIPTION OF COVER

1940 — Pansy Potter holds see-saw for other characters.

1941 — Beano folk appearing from giant egg.

1942 — Lord Snooty playing bagpipes.

1943 — Three-legged race.

1944 — Pillow-fight.

1945 — Ostrich-drawn cart.

1946 — Leap-frog.

1947 — Big Eggo swallowing cricket ball.

1948 — Big Eggo and others playing musical instruments.

1949 — Biffo and others around a taxi.

1950 — Biffo painting portrait.

1951 — Biffo rides mechanical horse.

1952 — Biffo nails pictures of characters to wall.

1953 — Jack Flash carries Biffo.

1954 — Biffo on a desert island.

1955 — Policeman stops Biffo and Dennis from fishing.

1956 — "General Jumbo" Biffo controls toy Beano figures.

1957 — Football match.

1958 — Biffo juggling.

1959 — Goat chases leap-frogging Little Plum.

1960 — Biffo completing jigsaw of Bash Street Kids.

1961 — Red cover with pictures of characters top and bottom.

1962 — Jonah dancing on mast of sinking ship.

1963 — Bash Street Kids on large swing.

1964 — Biffo holds bar-bell, being tickled with feather.

1965 — Little Plum and Minnie the Minx blowing up Biffo-head balloon.

You can use this guide to identify the annuals featured in the scenes at the beginning and end of this book.